MW00611195

Pursuing Your Calling

DEVELOP THE MISSIONAL HABITS OF A GLOBAL WORKER

FROM ENCOMPASS WORLD PARTNERS

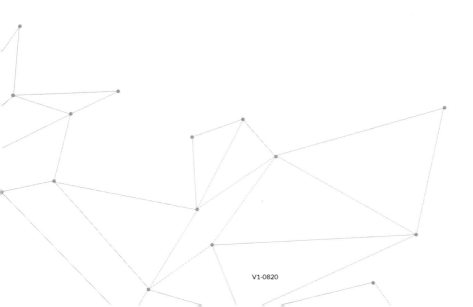

V1-0820

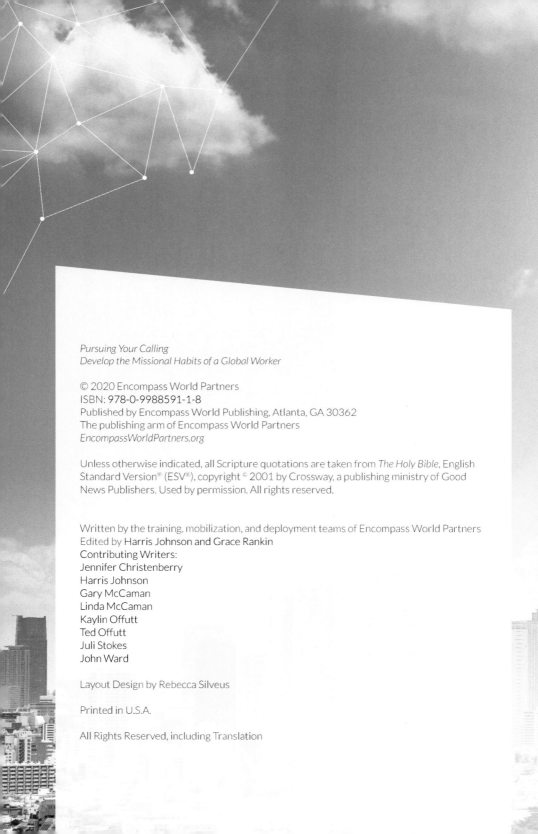

Pursuing Your Calling
Develop the Missional Habits of a Global Worker

© 2020 Encompass World Partners
ISBN: 978-0-9988591-1-8
Published by Encompass World Publishing, Atlanta, GA 30362
The publishing arm of Encompass World Partners
EncompassWorldPartners.org

Unless otherwise indicated, all Scripture quotations are taken from *The Holy Bible*, English Standard Version® (ESV®), copyright © 2001 by Crossway, a publishing ministry of Good News Publishers. Used by permission. All rights reserved.

Written by the training, mobilization, and deployment teams of Encompass World Partners
Edited by Harris Johnson and Grace Rankin
Contributing Writers:
Jennifer Christenberry
Harris Johnson
Gary McCaman
Linda McCaman
Kaylin Offutt
Ted Offutt
Juli Stokes
John Ward

Layout Design by Rebecca Silveus

Printed in U.S.A.

All Rights Reserved, including Translation

ABOUT THE SERIES

THE PATH: NAVIGATING THE JOURNEY TO GLOBAL MISSIONS

Travel tools and resources help us learn about destinations, give us insights, and point the way. Likewise, the titles in this series act as a map, a guide, and a compass to help you navigate the journey to global missions.

Start down the path to knowing God's heart for the nations and how you can become a part of His global mission.

Next steps on the path for those who are mobilizing individuals and teams into meaningful ministry to the nations.

Next steps on the path for potential cross-cultural workers discerning the call to make disciples among the nations.

ABOUT THE AUTHORS

THIS BOOK is a combined effort of the Encompass World Partners' training, mobilization, and deployment teams. It brings together the combined knowledge of decades of service among the least reached. We hope that this resource guides you on the path as you *pursue your calling*.

ABOUT THE AGENCY

ENCOMPASS WORLD PARTNERS was birthed in 1900 from a commitment to make disciples among all nations.

Its purpose is: To mobilize, equip, deploy, and nurture multinational teams of disciple-makers who live and proclaim the good news of Jesus Christ through engaging in sacrificial service, intentional evangelism, and whole-life discipleship, resulting in the creation of healthy spiritual communities (churches).

The rallying cry of Encompass World Partners is *more fruitful disciple-making teams among the least-reached peoples of our world.* Learn more about the ministries of Encompass and how you can become involved at EncompassWorldPartners.org.

TABLE OF CONTENTS

Introduction 9

Part 1 // GETTING STARTED 15

    Lesson 1 // LIFE PRIORITIES 17

    Lesson 2 // IDENTITY IN CHRIST 21

    Lesson 3 // THREE BOOKS 23

    Lesson 4 // RHYTHM AND SABBATH 29

    Lesson 5 // THIRD PLACES 33

    Lesson 6 // SELF-AWARENESS 37

    Lesson 7 // REFLECT AND PROCESS 41

Part 2 // GOING FURTHER 45

    Lesson 8 // CROSS-CULTURAL NOTEBOOK 47

    Lesson 9 // PASSION FOR MISSIONS 51

    Lesson 10 // LIFE TRANSFORMATION GROUPS 55

    Lesson 11 // PATHWAYS TO GOD 59

    Lesson 12 // SPIRITUAL WARFARE WITHIN ME 63

    Lesson 13 // CROSS-CULTURAL MINISTRY 67

    Lesson 14 // PHYSICAL HEALTH 71

    Lesson 15 // REFLECT AND PROCESS 75

Part 3 // FURTHER STILL 79

    Lesson 16 // SPIRITUAL GIFTS 81

    Lesson 17 // PROCESS EVANGELISM 85

    Lesson 18 // COMMUNITY 89

    Lesson 19 // ROOTS 93

    Lesson 20 // PEOPLE AND CULTURE 97

    Lesson 21 // FREEDOM OF SELF-FORGETFULNESS 101

    Lesson 22 // DAY WITH GOD 103

    Lesson 23 // SPIRITUAL WARFARE AROUND ME 107

    Lesson 24 // REFLECT AND PROCESS 111

Conclusion 115

Appendix 1 // BIBLICAL FOUNDATIONS 117

Appendix 2 // COMPETENCIES AND QUALIFICATIONS 123

What Can I Do to Prepare? 127

INTRODUCTION
DEVELOP THE MISSIONAL HABITS OF A GLOBAL WORKER

We are so glad that you are following God by pursuing your calling. In The Path series, this book serves as a compass, showing you how to develop missional habits now while you plan for future cross-cultural ministry.

Not everyone is ready to go the moment they feel God calling them to missions. The same reason it isn't recommended that you show up at the start of a marathon without training is the reason we've compiled these lessons—to prepare you for what you'll face as a global worker. Training is needed just to get to the starting line, much more to finish the race. The path to global missions is not a simple one and requires people who practice good missional habits. We're glad that you're using this resource to help you prepare for a fruitful, growing ministry.

HOW DO YOU LEARN GOOD MISSIONAL HABITS WHILE STAYING FOCUSED ON THE GOAL?

First, pursue your calling with passion, or a sense of purpose.
If you're confident that this is what God has called you to, then even adversity will not divert you from your goal. When you train for any sport, one of the biggest hurdles to overcome is your

own mind. Focusing on the goal instead of the other distractions makes all the difference. In missions, knowing your calling, seeing the need, and depending on Christ will help you to stay focused.

Second, lean on others who know what lies ahead. Pursuing your calling in global missions takes work, training, and focus. Seeking advice from others who have gone before you is critical. Those who have already pursued this path can share their knowledge with you. This is why we set this book up as a guide with lessons for you work through with a local mentor.

Third, focus your energy on what is important. Training for anything in life will have elements of difficulty and struggle. That's why focusing your energy on these missional habits will make you more effective both now and in the future. The challenges you'll face as you seek to apply these habits are a part of what you need to embrace as you pursue your calling. Don't expect to arrive at your goal without the difficulties and challenges of training. Practicing these missional habits will not only prepare you as a global worker, but the process you go through will also help you be more resilient when you face adversity.

Fourth, find others to partner with you and hold you accountable. Share your dreams with others and help them to understand and become invested in helping you get there. It is much easier to train with a coach or mentor. Work closely with your mentor through this book and let them cheer you on in your pursuit.

HOW TO USE THIS RESOURCE

This book includes 24 lessons covering eight missional habits. It is meant to be completed at a pace that works for you. It is designed to give you a cursory knowledge of the habits and practices you will learn and apply as you work through the lessons. Your church and missions agency may have additional training that they want you to gain beyond these lessons. If so, you can work with them on a plan to accomplish those training goals in addition to what you put into practice from this book.

Each lesson is divided into four sections. The first contains a few explanatory paragraphs that discuss the topic of the lesson and prepare you to answer questions. The second is comprised of a set of tasks; these may be questions you can journal about and answer, or they may be assignments that allow you to put into practice what you are learning. The third is a mentor discussion section; this is particularly where you can go through with your mentor and discuss the lesson and its implications on your life. The fourth and final section includes resources. These may be links, books to read, or online assessments that provide you with information for further study and growth.

While you go through this book, keeping a journal (digital or paper) where you can record your thoughts and questions will help you track your progress. As always, keep your Bible close at hand as well.

This book is meant to be used in conjunction with two key relationships:

// **A Local Mentor**, preferably from your church or a respected voice in cross-cultural ministry. Your church may have a designated person who helps prepare future global workers. If not, look for someone who demonstrates godly character and practices many of these missional habits.

// **A Mobilizer** who is there to walk with you through the process, helping you discern God's leading, discovering opportunities to serve, and affirming the right fit in cross-cultural ministry. If you don't have a mobilizer, you can email **GO@EncompassWorld.org**.

Among the listed resources in this book, there are several required titles. Below is a list of books you will want to have on hand as you make your way through this book:

- *Ministering Cross-Culturally* by Sherwood Lingenfelter and Marvin Mayers (Lesson 13)

- *The Freedom of Self-Forgetfulness* by Timothy Keller (Lesson 21)

- *Bondage Breaker* by Neil Anderson or *The Three Princes* by Tom Julien (Lesson 23)

After completing this book, you can use it as a reference guide while continuing a relationship with your mentor. It is not intended to provide a few boxes for you to check off, but rather to teach habits and practices that will continue to pattern your life as you pursue your calling. At the bottom of most lessons is a list of resources to help you dig deeper into these topics.

TIPS FOR MENTORS

Mentoring is a wonderful opportunity to encourage, teach, and equip future global workers. Remember that we all started somewhere, so don't expect your mentees to jump to where you are. Instead, put yourself in their shoes, recalling when you were their age. We recognize that many of you have been doing this for years while others are just getting started. Either way, we want to help you as you journey with your mentees.

> *What you have heard from me in the presence of many witnesses entrust to faithful men, who will be able to teach others also.*

2 Timothy 2:2

> *And let us consider how to stir up one another to love and good works, not neglecting to meet together, as is the habit of some, but encouraging one another, and all the more as you see the Day drawing near.*

Hebrews 10:24–25

HELPFUL TIPS:

// **Initiate.** Although we hope mentees will learn to be responsible for their growth throughout these lessons, you can help them by setting an example.

- Set up a regular time to meet. Weekly or bi-weekly meetings are suggested.

- Ensure the meeting time is prioritized and confirmed and that lessons to complete are determined beforehand.

// **Prepare.** Think through the meeting in advance.

- Plan a few aspects that will be a part of each meeting.

- Follow up on what has happened since the last time you met.

- Connect personally by sharing and asking them about how and what they are doing.

- Be honest and vulnerable.

- Determine with the mentees what lesson or lessons are next.

// **Participate.** Periodically engaging with mentees in the lessons can be one of the most powerful ways to mentor them.

- Go through the exercises yourself.

- Consider what your mentees are thinking and feeling.

- Observe their strengths and weaknesses.

- Offer encouragement.

- Communicate your commitment to them.

// **Model.** Invite mentees to participate in your ministry, especially when it reinforces a lesson they are learning.

- Do ministry together.

- Teach them practically with hands-on learning.

The Encompass World Partners' Team is available to work with you as you seek to walk through *Pursuing Your Calling* with your mentees. We will coach you on how to use this resource and answer any questions you have along the way. To set up a meeting with a member of the training team, send an email to GO@EncompassWorld.org. ●

INTRODUCING MISSIONAL HABITS

At the beginning of each lesson, there is a small icon at the top of the page. These icons correspond to the eight missional habits you will put into practice, sometimes repeatedly, throughout the 24 lessons in this book. Practicing these missional habits will allow you to thrive both in your personal and ministry life.

CONNECTING WITH GOD
Nurture your personal relationship with God.

PHYSICAL HEALTH
Care for your body by healthy eating, physical activity, and adequate rest.

CULTURAL INSIGHTS
Study the culture around you.

PROACTIVE DISCIPLE-MAKING
Encourage others to live as followers of Jesus in all aspects of their lives.

IDENTITY IN CHRIST
Recognize that your identity is based on who you are in Christ.

RHYTHM AND SABBATH REST
Live your life in healthy, life-giving rhythms.

LIVING IN COMMUNITY
Maintain mutual accountability in all aspects of your life.

SPIRITUAL WARFARE
Battle for God's truth in both your personal life and ministry.

PART 1
GETTING STARTED

LESSON 1
LIFE PRIORITIES

PLANNING A WEEKLY SCHEDULE

As believers with a heart for the lost, we likely have good intentions of building relationships with nonbelievers, living life and sharing with them. Likewise, we desire to encourage and be encouraged by other believers. Yet often a week, several weeks, and more can get away from us, and when we look back, we may be discouraged by how we've spent our time.

This lesson encourages the habit of strategically planning your week based on your top priorities. While strategy is emphasized here, we do not intend to minimize the Holy Spirit's work in your life and His prompting throughout the week. Sometimes He will move your heart to take unplanned action, and that is a good thing. The point of this lesson is to prepare you for day-to-day discipline in scheduling your life and accomplishing what you need to week by week.

TASKS:

Begin a routine of planning each week before you go into it.

1. **Determine the best time to sit down and plan the following week.**

   - Give yourself ample time (one to two hours).

   - Consider what day feels most natural to think through the next week.

   - Make sure you are free of other responsibilities.

2. **Have your calendar with you—paper or electronic.**

3. **Begin your schedule with your top priorities.**

   Watch this video: **https://bit.ly/PYCBigRocks**

   Think about how to incorporate each of these aspects into your week:

   - Work hours

   - Scheduled appointments

   - Sabbath rest

   - Family routines that involve set times, such as date night, school events, homework help, etc.

   - Time with God (quiet time)

   - Anything that already has a place on this week's calendar, such as a meeting, party, etc.

   - Meeting with your mentor

4. **Fill in other activities. Some items may be equally important but have more flexibility than those in the list above.**

   - Social time with life-giving people

   - Social time with nonbelievers (more on this later)

   - Prep time needed for mandatory activities (work, ministry, cooking/meal planning)

5. **Examine your remaining free time and determine the best fit for the following:**

   - Domestic chores

   - Proper, adequate rest

   - Personal hygiene

   - Ongoing projects

The "sand" (games, movies, social media, etc.) does not need to be planned, but will fall into the gaps left over.

The above bullet points will likely not cover everything on your weekly agenda, but they provide a helpful guideline for prioritizing as you schedule them.

Look at your complete week and ask questions:

- Does your schedule reflect your highest priorities?

- Are you trying to do too much or too little?

- Are you being realistic?

- What priorities or people are not in this week that you can make note of for upcoming weeks?

DISCUSS WITH YOUR MENTOR:

Show your first week's schedule to your mentor for feedback and discuss your thoughts and ideas with them. As time goes on, don't hesitate to ask your mentor for suggestions regarding your priorities and how to arrange your week accordingly.

RESOURCES:

The 7 Habits of Highly Effective People: Powerful Lessons in Personal Change
(25th Anniversary Edition) by Stephen Covey
Published by Simon & Schuster in New York, 2013.

"7 Big Rocks - The Productivity System" by Stephen Covey , found on *YouTube*, accessed August 3, 2020, **https://bit.ly/PYCBigRocks**.

YOUR THOUGHTS:

_____

_____

LESSON 2
IDENTITY IN CHRIST

FINDING YOUR IDENTITY AS A CHILD OF GOD

When asked "Who are you?" or "Tell me about yourself," we usually talk about visible realities of our lives: "I am a student"; "I am a mother of three"; "My profession is..."; "I grew up in..."; etc. These things and others are all true and make up a huge part of who we are. However, none of these categories represents who we really are.

The reality for any true follower of Christ is that his or her central identity is as a person who has been adopted by the Creator of the universe, a co-heir with Jesus, loved and completely accepted by the Father.

Whenever we wrongly prioritize our identity, we begin to walk a dangerous path. It causes us to search for our sense of self-worth in our success. "Am I a good father?" "Am I smarter than others?" This leads either to pride or self-deprecation.

One of the dangers of pursuing our calling in missions is seeking to find our identity in a role or title instead of simply being one who is loved by God.

TASKS:

- Prayerfully look at the passages that help you understand who you are in Christ (see link below).

- Begin a notebook on "My Identity in Christ." Here you can record truths that God says about you as well as ways you may be inappropriately seeking personal validation. Adding to this notebook from time to time will help you to see how Christ shapes your identity.

DISCUSS WITH YOUR MENTOR:

- Ask your mentor where they have mistakenly placed their identity at times.

- Share ways you are tempted to place your identity outside of Christ.

RESOURCES:

"Who I Am in Christ" by Michael Fackerell , found on *Christian-Faith*, **https://bit.ly/PYCWhoIam**.

YOUR THOUGHTS:

LESSON 3
THREE BOOKS

ORGANIZING YOUR PERSONAL MINISTRY

As believers, we desire to live in community with others, reaching out to those who do not know Christ and pointing them to Him.

Tom Julien, director of Encompass World Partners from 1986 to 2000, developed the Three Books idea during his 28 years as a missionary in France. He found that managing his many contacts, resource materials, and busy schedule became overwhelming. Recording each of these three categories of information into a separate "book" freed him from the pressure of storing it all in his head or scattering it across multiple places.

Thankfully, today we have many different ways (spreadsheets, client relationship managers [CRMs], and other apps) to manage all of this information. What is important is that you find a system that works for you and stick with it.

The Three Books do not need to be literal books. Rather, each one is a place where you record important information and your own thoughts. These "books" can be physical books, sections of a single notebook, or lists on an electronic device.

These Three Books give you a way to keep track of who you're working with, what steps have been taken with them, what the next steps are, and how everything fits into your daily schedule. This is similar to how psychiatrists and other professionals keep track of their relationships with clients. It is imperative, though, not to see people as projects. It is also important to note that we do not want people to see our notes on them, as this is a place for our own personal thoughts.

Book 1 – People: Nonbelievers you are reaching out to and believers you are discipling.

Book 2 – Resources: A growing collection of resources you have or that are available to use with your contacts and disciples.

Book 3 – Planning: Your weekly or monthly schedule.

TASKS:

Book 1: Everyone has a larger network than they realize. We have family members, neighbors, work colleagues, teammates, friends, social acquaintances, and others. These can even be people you interact with on an irregular basis like your hair stylist or the grocery store clerk. As believers, we desire that they would all know God and enjoy a relationship with Him. This tool helps us be intentional and strategic in sharing Christ with those in our lives.

- Determine your method (electronic, physical, etc.) and set it up.

- List all known contacts under either believers or not sure. A contact is anyone you will see repeatedly. These are people you are intentionally trying to build relationships with. You may or may not know if they are believers or nonbelievers.

- Pray regularly for your contacts. Pray for their hearts to be open, for God's Spirit to work in them, and for wisdom regarding your role in ministering to them.

- Note what you have learned about each person that would be valuable as you move forward. For example: open to spiritual conversations but has a negative view of the church; name of spouse or children; physical challenges.

- List the steps you have taken with them. Spiritual conversations or topics you have discussed, books, articles, or podcasts you have pointed them to or given to them, etc.

- With the last two points in mind, consider what might be a good next step. Some examples include inviting them to something, such as a social event, where they can meet other believers, or considering a conversation topic to bring up.

- Make a separate list of anyone you are currently discipling or believers you are influencing.

- List important information that will help you. (This is still Book 1, but you may certainly use another book or page on your electronic device if you choose.)

- List concepts or material you have discussed with them.

- Consider and note ideas, conversations, materials, or events that could be a next step for them.

Book 2: This is a list of the resources that you have used or that others have told you about. It could include books or Bible studies on different topics that come up frequently. Maybe you even have a list of your current library and who is borrowing what book.

Book 3: Set up your calendar/schedule. Remember what you learned in Lesson 1 about planning your weekly schedule. Prioritizing time with the people in Book 1 is the goal.

- If you do not regularly use a weekly calendar, determine what method would be a good fit for you: electronic apps, a calendar book, or a journal.

- For each person listed in Book 1, consider what would be a good next step, and determine a time to connect with that person. It is not necessary, and likely impossible, to schedule something for every contact each week. The principle is to use your contacts list to determine your weekly schedule.

- Consider your appointments and tasks for the week according to when people are available: people appointments first, tasks second.

DISCUSS WITH YOUR MENTOR:

- What is your initial reaction to the idea of the Three Books?

- Are you in the habit of being intentional in your approach to ministry?

- What do you anticipate will be the benefits of this approach?

- How does the Three Book approach help you prioritize time with your contacts?

- Choose a contact and discuss a possible next step with them.

YOUR THOUGHTS:

_____

_____

_____

_____

_____

_____

_____

_____

_____

_____

_____

_____

LESSON 4
RHYTHM AND SABBTH

MAKING TIME TO RELAX AND RECHARGE

The word Sabbath comes from the Hebrew word Shabbat, which means "to cease." This is a time to disengage from our normal activities in order to rest, connect with God, and spend time with life-giving people in life-giving activities.

God set the rhythm of six to one in creation and in the Sabbath for the nation of Israel. Though we are not under law to keep the Sabbath, it is a gift to us to make sure we get the rest we need, deepen our relationship with God, and slow down in life. A weekly day of rest (and other times of retreat) is an act of worship that we should practice regularly.

TASKS:

We do not want to be legalistic and make a list of dos and don'ts for your Sabbath day, but considering your answers to these questions will help you plan your day of rest.

- What activities refresh or energize you?

- Who is life-giving to you? (Spending time with them refuels you.)

- What role does sleep play? (Freedom to sleep in or take a nap is helpful.)

- What activities are taxing to you, yet you often tend to do on your "day off"?

- While brainstorming the "perfect" day off can be inspiring, remember that the goal is to rest weekly. What is practical?

- How can you incorporate worship into your day?

- Determine what day of the week will be your day off. List things that will be a part of this day.

DISCUSS WITH YOUR MENTOR:

Talk about your answers to the questions above, and then consider these further questions with your mentor:

* It is said that busyness is the one sin Christians praise. How do you react to this statement?

* What is your current routine of rest or ceasing?

* Does your week have a set, clear day of rest?

Now, enjoy your weekly Sabbath!

RESOURCES:

"Wisdom and Sabbath Rest" by Timothy Keller, found on *Gospel in Life*, accessed August 3, 2020, **https://bit.ly/PYCSabbathRest**.

Soul Custody: Choosing to Care for the One and Only You by Stephen W. Smith Published by David C. Cook in Colorado Springs, 2010.

YOUR THOUGHTS:

_____

_____

_____

_____

_____

_____

_____

LESSON 5
THIRD PLACES

CONSIDERING HOBBIES AND HANGOUTS WITH INTENTIONALITY

Third Place is a term used in the concept of community-building, referring to social surroundings separate from the usual environments of home and work (or school). Third Places are where people who share common interests choose to gather with others. Anywhere one can be with the same people on a regular basis, engage in conversation, and build relationships, these places provide great opportunities to live life together and exchange ideas. Participating in Third Places allows us to build relational bridges naturally through common interests.

Chances are you are already engaged in what could be considered a Third Place. The best kind of place is somewhere you have genuine interest. This might even be a place that you are worried isn't "spiritual" enough, like a sports team, board game group, gym membership, theatre troupe, pottery class, book club, etc. God never said that you can't do things that you enjoy while building relationships with others with whom to share the gospel. The more you can show excellence and good sportsmanship/encouragement, pointing to God as the supplier of your success, the better.

TASKS:

- What are your current Third Places?

- What Third Places have you been involved in before, perhaps not realizing they were a Third Place?

- What Third Places could you join to have cross-cultural experiences?

- What could you do in your current Third Places to be more effective?

- What might you need to give up to engage with more unbelievers?

- How do you anticipate this ministry approach to be effective?

DISCUSS WITH YOUR MENTOR:

- Think through your regular activities. Are you involved in a Third Place?

- Are you using it to build relationships? Discuss with your mentor if this is a good Third Place for you and how you are building relationships with people there.

- Discuss your interests and skills. Based on those, develop a list of three to five potential Third Places in your area.

If you are not already involved in a Third Place that is a good fit for you, choose one of the Third Places on your list in which to participate. After a few visits, evaluate with your mentor its effectiveness in building intentional relationships.

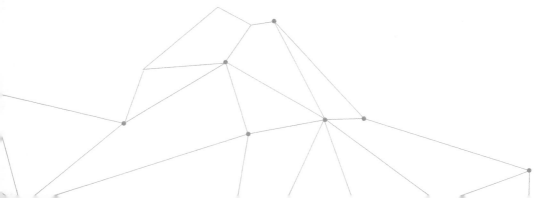

RESOURCES:

"What Is a Third Place and Why Do You Need One?" *The Third Place: The Importance of Ray Oldenburg's Third Place* on *The Art of Charm* by Johnny Dzubak, found on *The Art of Charm*, accessed August 3, 2020, **https://bit.ly/PYCThirdSpaces**.

YOUR THOUGHTS:

_____

_____

_____

_____

_____

_____

_____

_____

_____

_____

_____

_____

_____

_____

LESSON 6
SELF-AWARENESS

DISCOVERING WHO YOU ARE AND LEARNING WHO KNOWS YOU

You have been developing in your understanding and ability to live out of your identity in Christ. This is essential for life and ministry as you continue learning.

Second to this is developing your understanding of who God has made you to be. This includes your personality, skills and abilities, passions and interests, spiritual gifts, strengths you bring to any situation, and ways you need others to provide balance where you are weak. Growing in self-awareness in each of these areas positions you now and in the future for maximum fruitfulness for God's kingdom.

There are many personality assessments available today. You may have already completed one or more as part of a school or work experience. The idea is to gain understanding and grow in self-awareness, not to put a label on yourself. Remember, only God truly understands you, so with that in mind, enjoy the experience of His Spirit revealing your uniqueness to you.

TASKS:

Take one of these assessments that you have not before and prepare to talk about it with your mentor.

The Clifton Strengths assessment - Strengthsfinder 2.0
($20 cost for the top five):
http://bit.ly/PYCStrengthsFinder

The High Five Test (similar to Strengthsfinder but free):
http://bit.ly/PYCHigh5Test

Myers-Briggs Type Indicator (free):
http://bit.ly/PYC16personalities

Enneagram (free):
https://bit.ly/PYCEnneagramfree

Examine the results of your assessment and think through the following questions:

a. What do you agree with and why? Think of examples in your life to support your conclusions.

b. What have you learned about yourself as a result of this assessment?

c. In what ways do you see yourself differently?

d. How will this knowledge affect your life moving forward?

e. What do you disagree with and why?

f. What words would you use to describe yourself instead? Think of examples in your life to support these descriptions.

DISCUSS WITH YOUR MENTOR:

Share your assessment results with your mentor, and ask them the following questions (at this point, refrain from sharing your opinion on your results):

- What do you see in me that aligns with these results? Ask for examples.

- What do you see in the results that isn't accurate with how you see me?

Share your thoughts and feelings about the results (answers to a–f) with your mentor and discuss the following questions:

- How were your responses the same as your mentor's?

- In what ways do you see things differently?

What is one way you will apply what you have just learned? Your mentor may be able to help you think through this step.

- How do you more clearly see your positive traits?

- How do you more clearly see your negative traits?

- How will this knowledge affect your life moving forward?

RESOURCES:

Now, Discover Your Strengths by Marcus Buckingham and Donald O. Clifton Published by The Free Press in New York, 2001.

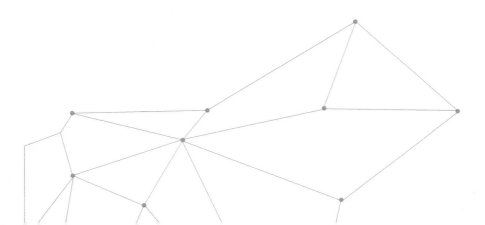

YOUR THOUGHTS:

_____

_____

_____

_____

_____

_____

_____

_____

_____

LESSON 7
REFLECT AND PROCESS

Take some time to process the last six lessons and how they have helped you develop missional habits. Please take the time to go back and look at those lessons, considering the things you have applied in your life.

- How has the new routine you learned from Lesson 1 changed your schedule to better represent your priorities?

- How has journaling helped you to learn more about your identity in Christ?

- Have you determined your method for the Three Books? How is it helping you prioritize your time?

- How has your regular Sabbath been? How has this weekly practice strengthened your spiritual walk?

- Have you implemented a new Third Place or seen how to utilize a current one to develop new, intentional relationships?

- How have you applied what you learned about yourself in Lesson 6 on self-awareness?

Look back on the last six lessons.

- Is there anything that you would like to better implement in your daily routine? What steps will you take to do that?

- Before continuing to the next section, talk with your mentor about what next steps you want to take.

YOUR THOUGHTS:

_____

_____

_____

_____

_____

_____

_____

_____

_____

_____

_____

_____

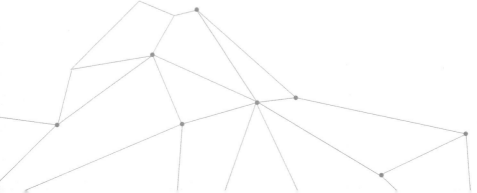

PART 2
GOING FURTHER

LESSON 8

CROSS-CULTURAL NOTEBOOK

LEARNING TO RECOGNIZE OTHER CULTURES AND THEIR NORMS

Merriam-Webster defines culture as, "the customary beliefs, social forms, and material traits of a racial, religious, or social group."[1] Here is a simpler definition: the ways that a people group thinks and acts.

This group may be as small as a family or as large as a nation. Just as every family has its own way of doing things—a culture— so larger groups (people groups within a country, citizens of a geographical country) exhibit their own culture. Generally, we expect people to behave in the same way that we do. Imagine meeting someone for the first time and extending your hand for a handshake, only to be pulled into a hug and a kiss on the cheek. How would you react? That is a minor example of a difference in cultures.

[1] *Merriam-Webster*, s.v. "culture," accessed July 29, 2020. https://www.merriam-webster.com/dictionary/culture.

You have likely noticed distinctions in the people around you, but maybe without processing them. Or perhaps you've found yourself thinking, "These people are strange. I don't know why anyone would do that." But strange according to what guidelines? This is a judgment based on your own cultural habits and values—it's subjective.

When we view other cultures, this truth should guide us: culture is often neither good nor bad, just different.

TASKS:

- Begin a cross-cultural notebook in which you write down cultural differences you observe.

- Look for places where you can encounter people of diverse cultures and spend time there. Depending on where you live, this may be as simple as going to a local park or grocery store. How do families interact? Who cares for the children? What types of food are purchased? Who chooses the food? Who pays?

- Look for opportunities to make friends with people from other cultures. As you notice different ways of doing things, you can discuss these differences. Ask them what they find strange about your culture.

DISCUSS WITH YOUR MENTOR:

- Discuss these cultural differences with your mentor.

- Have they noticed the same things?

- Have they made different observations?

Noticing cultural differences will become a lifelong habit. This will help you better understand others and effectively share Christ with them.

RESOURCES:

Foreign to Familiar: A Guide to Understanding Hot- and Cold-Climate Cultures
by Sarah A. Lanier
Published by McDougal Publishing in Hagerstown, MD, 2000.

American Cultural Baggage: How to Recognise and Deal With It
by Stan Nussbaum
Published by Orbis Books in Maryknoll, NY, 2005.

YOUR THOUGHTS:

LESSON 9
PASSION FOR MISSIONS

STOKING THE FIRE

Keeping the passion for missions alive over time can be difficult. We can compare the passion for missions to a fire that needs to be tended.

If you were in Boy or Girl Scouts, or some other outdoor club, you likely learned the four steps to building a fire:

1. Start with **kindling**
2. Keep it **dry**
3. Feed it **soft woods**, then **hard woods**
4. Give it **oxygen**

Start the passion for missions with small, easy steps that burn quickly but produce heat, like a weeklong trip overseas. Next, keep the vision dry from barriers and difficulties, such as the ease of living a "normal" life, which will quickly douse the flame. Then, sustain the fire with softwood, like attending seminars and watching videos, and then with increasingly harder woods, like leading and teaching others. Finally, fan and stoke the fire to keep it going strong by learning new skills and preparing for future ministry. The tasks in this lesson will help you to evaluate what stage your passion is at and how to keep it growing.

TASKS:

- What are/were the early stages of heat that started your fire for missions?

- What are some elements that may tempt your passion to wane?

- What are some "softwoods" that you have used on your fire or that you could use?

DISCUSS WITH YOUR MENTOR:

- With your mentor, discuss what stage you think your passion is at.

- Talk to your mentor about more of the "hardwoods" they have used and if/how you can be involved in those.

- How will you keep fanning or stoking the fire of your passion for missions?

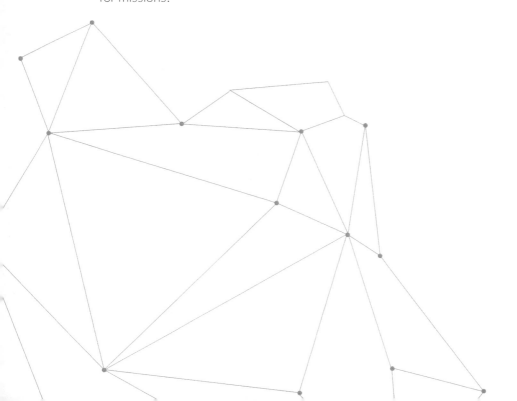

RESOURCES:

CROSS Conference: http://bit.ly/PYCCrossCon

Through Gates of Splendor by Elisabeth Elliot
Published by Tyndale Momentum, updated revised edition, 2002.

The Insanity of God: A True Story of Faith Resurrected by Nik Ripken
Published by B&H Publishing Group in Nashville, TN, 2013.

The Insanity of Obedience: Advancing the Gospel When Facing Challenges and Persecution by Nik Ripken
Published by LifeWay Press, 2016.

YOUR THOUGHTS:

LESSON 10

LIFE TRANSFORMATION GROUPS

CHALLENGING EACH OTHER WITH LIFE-ON-LIFE LIVING

Life Transformation Groups (LTGs) are designed to promote spiritual growth in a context of mutual accountability. The design is simple. A group of three or four people of the same gender meet on a weekly basis to hold one another accountable to reading Scripture, living for Christ, and reaching out to others.

LTGs are a form of peer discipleship. These groups are all about intentional relationships as group members pursue God and work to be purposeful with others. Through prayer and personal challenge, they help each other grow in evangelism and discipleship of those God puts on their hearts. These groups are not meant to take the place of church small groups, which are usually much larger and include both men and women.

Here are a few general guidelines for LTGs:

- The ideal size is three to four people, which allows for all members of the group to share and does not require a trained person to run the meetings.

- Participants should be of the same gender.

- Groups should meet once a week for about an hour.

- Members ask questions of each other regarding their walk with Christ during the week. They may choose to use a list of prepared questions, write their own, or use a combination.

- Groups choose passages or entire books of the Bible to read during the week. Members record their personal observations and share these during the LTG meeting.

- Confidentiality is essential to LTGs. What is shared in the LTG stays between its members.

TASKS:

- Pray about who you might ask to join you in an LTG and discuss it with your mentor.

- Invite people to join you in forming an LTG. Choose what you will read and what questions you will ask each other.

- Continue it long enough to make it a lifelong habit.

DISCUSS WITH YOUR MENTOR:

- How could peer discipleship like this be encouraging in your life?

- Who are the three to five people that you would like to be accountable for as you seek to share the gospel?

- How have groups like this been encouraging in your mentor's life?

- Who could you invite to join you in an LTG?

RESOURCES:

"Life Transformation Groups (LTGs)" on *Missional Challenge* by Dave DeVries, found on *Missional Challenge*, accessed August 3, 2020, **https://bit.lyPYCLifeGroup**.

Cultivating a Life for God: Multiplying Disciples Through Life Transformation Groups by Neil Cole
Published by Church Smart Resources, 1999.

YOUR THOUGHTS:

_____

_____

_____

_____

_____

_____

_____

LESSON 11

PATHWAYS TO GOD

LEARNING HOW YOU BEST CONNECT WITH GOD

In an earlier lesson, you were tasked with taking a personality test. Such assessments help us understand our unique personality. But have you considered that you also have a unique way that you connect with God?

While it is important to study God's Word and spend time in prayer, have you considered other ways to spend time with Him? Discovering your particular "pathway" may free you to spend time with God in a variety of ways. God created you with unique talents, abilities, and interests. He enjoys spending time with His children, and your pathway is another level on which you and your heavenly Father can connect.

The nine Pathways to God are addressed in **Sacred Pathways** by Gary Thomas p. 23-30[2]:

- **Intellectual** – Loving God with the Mind

- **Contemplative** – Loving God Through Adoration

- **Enthusiast** – Loving God with Mystery and Celebration

- **Caregiver** – Loving God by Loving Others

- **Activist** – Loving God Through Confrontation

- **Naturalist** – Loving God Out of Doors

- **Traditionalist** – Loving God Through Ritual and Symbol

- **Sensate** – Loving God with the Senses

- **Ascetic** – Loving God in Solitude and Simplicity

As you consider this, it's important to remember that God has also told us not to forsake gathering together. Your pathway does not take the place of corporate times of worship and prayer with fellow believers. The pathway is simply understanding the ways that you connect with God as an individual.

TASKS:

Use the following assessment to help you determine what pathways you may have: **http://bit.ly/PYCPathways**

You should note the two or three pathways in which you received a high score. Sometimes there are ways to combine two pathways, such as journaling while being out in nature.

- Gary Thomas. *Sacred Pathways: Discovering Your Soul's Path to God* (Grand Rapids: Zondervan, 2010), 23-30.

DISCUSS WITH YOUR MENTOR:

- Think and discuss practical ways you can lean into your pathways.

- Consider how your pathways will influence your planning of a weekly schedule.

- Share your pathways with your mentor and ask them to share theirs.

- Talk about how this might free you to see how you can engage more with God through your pathway.

RESOURCES:

Sacred Pathways: Discovering Your Soul's Path to God by Gary Thomas
Published by Zondervan in Grand Rapids, MI, 2010.

YOUR THOUGHTS:

LESSON 12

SPIRITUAL WARFARE WITHIN ME

DISCERNING SPIRITUAL REALITIES AND DISCOVERING HOW TO COMBAT THEM

While this idea is unpopular in select Christian circles, demonic attacks and forces are real. The battle is in and for the mind, heart, and soul. Recognizing the battle and the effect these forces have on us is an important step in the fight. They often come in the form of our own voice tempting us to do what we know is wrong. Spiritual obstacles must be overcome by spiritual means.

During His earthly ministry, Christ demonstrated total authority over demonic forces, and His death and resurrection mark their complete defeat. When He was tempted, Christ gave a two-pronged answer to Satan. First, He quoted Scripture, and second, He commanded Satan to leave (Matthew 4:10). We can use this effective pattern as well.

In James 4:7 we are told to, *"Submit yourselves therefore to God. Resist the devil, and he will flee from you."* We must make sure we are in the Scriptures daily and communicating with God, not giving the demons an open door, and actively resist temptations by commanding them to leave in Jesus' name.

If there is an area of our lives that we struggle in, it is best to remove ourselves from the situation. In Matthew 18:9, Jesus says, *"And if your eye causes you to sin, tear it out and throw it away. It is better for you to enter life with one eye than with two eyes to be thrown into the hell of fire."* This may mean that we need to give up our smartphone or an unhealthy relationship or change any number of things in our lives. We also need to confess sin to those that we have hurt or broken trust with as well as confess to God.

TASKS:

- Read Ephesians 6:11-18. In this passage, the Apostle Paul talks about preparing for spiritual warfare by wearing the full armor of God.

- You may want to track spiritual warfare and what you are learning about it. Keeping a notebook where you can write down your experiences and pray about them is a great way to do this.

- What will it mean to practice submitting your life to God and resisting the demons that persecute you?

- Pray for victory in the spiritual battles that you experience, but remember, you are not on even ground; you are on the winning side already.

DISCUSS WITH YOUR MENTOR:

- What does it mean to submit yourself to God?

- What does Paul mean when he says to wear the full armor of God?

- As you spend time writing in your notebook, record incidents of spiritual warfare in your life and discuss them with your mentor.

RESOURCES:

**The Steps to Freedom in Christ: A Biblical Guide to Help You Resolve
Personal and Spiritual Conflicts and Become a Fruitful Disciple of Jesus**
by Neil T. Anderson
Published by Bethany House Publishers in Bloomington, MN, 2017.

The Beginner's Guide to Spiritual Warfare by Neil T. Anderson
and Timothy M. Warner
Published by Bethany House Publishers, 2008.

"Spiritual Warfare: Part 1 & 2" by Allistair Begg, found on *YouTube*, accessed
August 3, 2020, **http://bit.ly/PYCSpiritualWar**.

YOUR THOUGHTS:

LESSON 13
CROSS-CULTURAL MINISTRY

SERVING GOD IN ANOTHER CULTURE AND CONTEXT

When people express nervousness about traveling abroad, they often receive the well-intentioned advice, "Just be yourself."

The problem with this advice lies in how many "selves" we are each day. Depending on our social context, we act differently. Think of how you behave in an elevator—you face the door, don't look at anyone, and certainly don't engage with your co-riders. Compare this with how you conduct yourself at funerals, church potlucks, or Super Bowl parties. The problem is, when in an entirely new culture, how do you know which "self" you should be? What are the norms for each of these situations in another culture?

You might object, "But that's all me...I just know how to behave in different social situations."

True, but the point is, your behavior is radically different depending on your social context. It's almost like you adopt different personalities.

The problem is the rules are often quite different when you switch cultures. If you respond as you would in your home culture, at best you might be an odd and somewhat rude person. At worst, you might seriously offend the people you are trying to minister to.

To get you started learning how cultures are different:

TASKS:

- Read the book *Ministering Cross-Culturally* by Sherwood Lingenfelter and Marvin Mayers.

- Make three copies of the Basic Values Questionnaire, the Analysis of Answers, and the personal profile (Chapter 2).

- Complete one of the questionnaires.

- Pray for God to lead you to two people from other cultures who are fluent in your language and ask them to complete the questionnaire. Think about the differences between your cultures.

DISCUSS WITH YOUR MENTOR:

- Talk about your questionnaire results and what insights you have gained.

- What would you find challenging about working in the cultures you interviewed?

RESOURCES:

Ministering Cross-Culturally: A Model for Effective Personal Relationships
by Sherwood G. Lingenfelter and Marvin K. Mayers
Published by Baker Academic in Grand Rapids, MI, 2016.

YOUR THOUGHTS:

_____

_____

_____

_____

_____

_____

_____

_____

LESSON 14
PHYSICAL HEALTH

CARING FOR YOUR BODY AS WELL AS YOUR SOUL

> *"Or do you not know that your body is a temple of the Holy Spirit within you, whom you have from God? You are not your own, for you were bought with a price. So glorify God in your body."*

1 Corinthians 6:19-20

God created us as holistic beings, and as such, we should care for ourselves spiritually, emotionally, mentally, and physically. This lesson deals only with your physical health since the other areas are covered in other lessons. Taking care of your body will allow you to serve the Lord for the long haul.

When it comes to our bodies, there are three categories of care. The first is staying active. In today's virtually driven culture, all the screen time compounded by working from a computer and sitting while driving means that the average person spends too much time standing and sitting still. God created us for movement, and our bodies and muscles need that movement to remain healthy.

The second is having self-control over what we eat and how much. In Babylon, Daniel and his friends purposed not to eat the king's foods which were against God's rules for His people and did not help them develop. After the test, Daniel and his friends were so much healthier that the king's steward took away the king's food from the other young men (Daniel 1:12-16).

The third is getting adequate sleep. Most high-achieving adults sleep between seven and nine hours a night. Our bodies need time to recharge and repair. Without that time, we don't have the regeneration we need, and our bodies start to break down. Sleep deprivation is a common tactic of interrogation used to break people—don't deprive yourself.

TASKS:

Caring for your physical health is an important part of developing good missional habits. We've created a table to help you evaluate and take steps to improve your physical health.

- Answer the questions in the table below about your physical health.

WHAT	EVALUATION – HOW AM I DOING IN THIS AREA?	WHAT STEPS SHOULD I TAKE (IF ANY) TO GROW/ IMPROVE?
Fitness: This can be measured by endurance (cardiovascular fitness), strength, flexibility, and agility. It is a good idea to get some form of physical exercise at least three times a week.	Am I getting regular exercise? Are there areas that I should address (endurance, strength, flexibility, agility)? Are there physical activities I could do that I enjoy and that wouldn't feel like a chore?	

WHAT	EVALUATION – HOW AM I DOING IN THIS AREA?	WHAT STEPS SHOULD I TAKE (IF ANY) TO GROW/ IMPROVE?
Internal Health: Things like blood sugar levels, cholesterol levels, blood pressure, etc., are best determined by getting a regular physical exam that includes blood tests.	When was the last time I had a physical exam? If it has been awhile, this should be a priority. As a result of the exam, are there things I need to change or do?	
Diet: There are many different ideas when it comes to the word "diet." You can determine what this means for you, but in general, it is a good idea to eat fewer saturated fats, more fruits and vegetables, minimal processed foods, and as little processed sugar as possible. Your diet will largely affect your overall health. A poor diet can lead to many issues such as obesity, diabetes, anemia, etc.	Am I eating too much or too little? Is my diet primarily comprised of whole foods with a good amount of vitamin-rich vegetables and fruits? Are there any foods that I should avoid or get more of?	
Sleep: It is recommended that one sleeps about eight hours a night for optimal health and alertness.	Am I sleeping well? If not, what do I need to change to address this? What changes can I make to enable me to get about eight hours of sleep a night?	

DISCUSS WITH YOUR MENTOR:

- Talk about your findings with your mentor and together develop a plan to improve in one of these areas.

- Ask your mentor to hold you accountable for this change in your lifestyle.

RESOURCES:

Eat Move Sleep: How Small Choices Lead to Big Changes by Tom Rath
Published by Missionday, 2013.

YOUR THOUGHTS:

LESSON 15
REFLECT AND PROCESS

- What is different about your life since you started practicing these missional habits?

- Have you found opportunities to add to your "Identity in Christ" notebook? How has it been helpful to you?

- Do you frequent a new Third Place? What relationships are you building there?

- How are you seeking a healthy rhythm and protecting your Sabbath?

- Have you become more intentional in your conversations with people from other cultures? Think of some examples of conversations you've had throughout this journey.

- What pathway(s) have you included in your weekly schedule? How has that been a helpful addition to your regular disciplines?

- What other lessons come to mind that have changed the way you think and live?

Take time to answer some of these questions and consider a few of the things you have intended to implement but haven't yet for one reason or another.

Talk with your mentor about what next steps you want to take before continuing to the next section.

YOUR THOUGHTS:

_____

_____

_____

_____

_____

_____

_____

_____

_____

_____

_____

_____

_____

_____

_____

PART 3
FURTHER STILL

LESSON 16
SPIRITUAL GIFTS

LEARNING HOW GOD HAS EQUIPPED YOU TO SERVE THE BODY OF CHRIST

In this lesson, you will continue to grow in your self-awareness by examining your spiritual gifts. God has given you skills, abilities, passions, and interests, and because you are His child and have the indwelling Holy Spirit, Scripture affirms that He has given you spiritual gifts as well.

These gifts are given to all believers and are the manifestation of His nature. They are given for the common good so that God's people are equipped for the good works He has planned for every one of His children. The best way to discover your spiritual gifting is to be involved in a variety of ministries that give you experience on which to base your understanding. If you have not already tried a variety of ministries, consider diversifying your experience and taking on something new.

TASKS:

- Read through 1 Corinthians 12, Romans 12:3-8, and Ephesians 4:1-13. As you read these passages, list any gifts you might have. Give examples of how you have used these gifts to build up of the body of Christ. This could include serving in your church or another ministry setting, sharing your time or resources to help bring others to faith, etc.

- Take this free survey **http://bit.ly/PYCSpiritualGifts**, or ask your mentor or a church leader if there is another spiritual gifts inventory they would recommend. APEST is a popular survey that costs $10 and is based on the gifts listed in Ephesians 4:11: **http://bit.ly/PYCAPEST**.

DISCUSS WITH YOUR MENTOR:

- After you take a spiritual gifts inventory, share your results with your mentor and discuss how you and they have observed you using these gifts. Take time to reflect on the three Bible passages listed above with your mentor.

- If you don't have examples of you using your spiritual gifts, talk with your mentor about how you can try a variety of ministry opportunities. As you use your gifts, it will help confirm if this is a gift God has given to you, and He will direct you in how to use it even more.

RESOURCES:

5Q: Reactivating the Original Intelligence and Capacity of the Body of Christ by Alan Hirsch
Published by 100 Movements, 2017.

YOUR THOUGHTS:

LESSON 17
PROCESS EVANGELISM

SHARING THE GOSPEL IN WORD AND DEED

> *"But in your hearts honor Christ the Lord as holy, always being prepared to make a defense to anyone who asks you for a reason for the hope that is in you; yet do it with gentleness and respect."*

1 Peter 3:15

By now you have discovered a Third Place and have hopefully had opportunities to get acquainted with people who don't yet know and follow Jesus. As you get to know them and learn what they are passionate about, look for opportunities to share Jesus, "the hope that is in you." One way of doing that is by sharing how Jesus has changed your life.

While we should be prepared to share a clear presentation of the gospel, most of our evangelistic work is like that of a farmer. We plant and water the seed, but it is God who brings about the harvest. Therefore, evangelism is more like an agricultural process than simply presenting the gospel and expecting instant results. As Paul says in 1 Corinthians 3:6, "I planted, Apollos watered, but God gave the growth. So neither he who plants nor he who waters is anything, but only God who gives the growth."

As you interact with people, listen to them and their stories. After you listen, share a relevant story of how Jesus has made the difference in your life. Invite them to read a story from the Bible that is relevant to the questions they have about life. Ask the Holy Spirit to water the seeds of faith that you've planted, and continue watering those seeds yourself with prayers for that person. You may be planting many seeds over time before it becomes evident that they are eager to know more about Jesus. When that time comes, be ready to invite them to follow Him.

TASKS:

- Write out your story of how you came to know and follow Jesus. Include versions that can be shared over longer and shorter periods of time. (2-7 minutes)

- Ask a trusted, believing friend if you can practice sharing your story and gospel presentation with them.

- Read Luke 12:11-12. Why are these verses comforting as you think about sharing your faith?

- Look for and pray for moments to share your story with a non-believing friend.

DISCUSS WITH YOUR MENTOR:

- Talk to your mentor about gospel presentation styles and find one that you are comfortable using.

- Pray about those contacts from your Book 1 that you would like to share this gospel presentation with and next steps you're praying they will take.

RESOURCES:

"3 Ways to Share the Gospel This Week" by Matt Smethurst, found on *The Gospel Coalition,* **http://bit.ly/PYC3WaystoShare**.

CRU has produced digital ministry tools to help Christians share their faith with their friends: **http://bit.ly/PYCEVtools**.

YOUR THOUGHTS:

_____

_____

_____

_____

_____

_____

_____

_____

_____

_____

_____

_____

_____

LESSON 18
COMMUNITY

PREPARING A TEAM OF SENDERS AND PARTNERS

> *"Two are better than one, because they have a good reward for their toil. For if they fall, one will lift up his fellow. But woe to him who is alone when he falls and has not another to lift him up!"*

Ecclesiastes 4:9-10

It is important that in your earnest desire to get to the mission field, you don't forget who you are and where you come from. How many of your high school friends do you still communicate with beyond social media interaction? How about college or past churches you attended? If you have moved a lot in your life, how have you maintained relationships with those you left?

Sometimes as people plan to make a transition, they start to pull back from their friends. This is a natural defense mechanism to prevent pain from loss. However, you will need these relationships not only for encouragement in your transition to a new culture but also for prayer and financial support.

TASKS:

- Read Proverbs 13:20 and 27:17.

- List people who you want to keep up with after you move and plan regular times to call or meet with them. This will help the time become an established habit that will follow you.

- Who are you bringing with you on this journey toward cross-cultural ministry? Do they have permission to speak difficult truths into your life as you discern your next steps?

- Friendships are about authenticity. Have a list of prayer requests ready. Be honest about your struggles so your friends can pray for you and understand that you need them as you move ahead.

- Think about past meaningful relationships that have drifted apart because one of you moved away. Consider how you can maintain or restart those relationships.

The more you let your friends in and remain open to them, the more they can encourage you in order to help you with your next steps. It may take years to build relationships in your new country to the point that you can trust their counsel, and you will need your friends to help you through the difficult transitions ahead.

DISCUSS WITH YOUR MENTOR:

- Discuss your current relationships with friends and family and how you want to manage those.

- Talk about how to best manage the relationship with your sending church.

RESOURCES:

"True Friends Are Hard to Find" by Kelly Needham, found on *DesiringGod*, http://bit.ly/PYCTrueFriend.

"5 Ways to Make Your Friendships More Christ-Centered" by Laura Pinckard, found on *Word of Life Bible Institute*, http://bit.ly/PYCFCC.

YOUR THOUGHTS:

_____

_____

_____

_____

_____

_____

_____

_____

_____

_____

_____

_____

_____

LESSON 19
ROOTS

LIVING IN THE HERE AND NOW WHILE PREPARING FOR THE FUTURE

If you had a date and an airline ticket—something concrete that defined how many days remained in your current place, job, house, role, etc.—planning for your departure would be easier. But at this stage in your journey, it's less likely that you have a date set. When the future is uncertain, it's tempting to allow your roots to grow deeper where you are.

Have you ever tried to transplant something? Small plants with healthy roots are rather easy to transplant. But a large plant with roots that go deep or far are nearly impossible to dig up without tearing the roots, and likewise are more difficult to re-root after being transplanted.

Until you have that date, it's important to be a part of your community with a level of stability—to have roots that will sustain you. Let's consider, however, how to be healthy without allowing those roots to go so deep that they hinder your hopeful transition into cross-cultural ministry.

TASKS:

Answer these questions for each of the following areas...

Finances are among the biggest barriers to those preparing to serve in missions.

1. What are you presently investing in that will be difficult to give up? (Such as a family business.)

2. What investments are lessening your financial freedom? (Think properties owned, etc.)

3. What financial obligations do you currently have? (Parents or others who might rely on you.)

4. What financial obligations should you avoid? (Taking on debts or responsibility of others, for example.)

Relationships are important and worthy of investment, but consider what you are communicating in these relationships.

1. Are you periodically communicating that your time here is limited? (Reminding people that you are planning to move overseas.)

2. In what relationships have you avoided sharing about your future? (Friends who you worry would not continue a relationship, family who might be disappointed in your decision, etc.)

3. In what relationships might you have set up an expectation of ongoing help or involvement? (Parents, older people in church, siblings, etc.)

Commitments are important to evaluate in the time needed to prepare for cross-cultural ministry.

1. While being involved and helping others is important, are there areas in which you need to communicate that your help is temporary, areas in which you should start to pull back? (Classes you are teaching, Bible studies, discipleship, etc.)

2. What are some areas such as school or projects that might tie you down longer than you want? (Grad school, missions training, etc.)

DISCUSS WITH YOUR MENTOR:

Allow these questions to help you process this idea of putting down roots. Ask your mentor what areas may need to be addressed as you pursue your calling in global missions.

YOUR THOUGHTS:

LESSON 20
PEOPLE AND CULTURE

RESEARCHING A PEOPLE GROUP OR CULTURE

You may have an idea of where you hope to minister, or you may simply know that God is calling you to another culture, but you don't yet know where. Speak with a mobilizer in order to learn of unreached or least-reached people groups who need workers. This may help you discern what direction to pursue.

As you move toward missions, learn about the people group and culture in which you are planning to minister. Researching now will help you determine if this is where God is calling you and help you begin to learn about this new culture. If you don't have a specific people group or country in mind, you may for the purpose of this lesson choose one in which you are interested or perhaps one that is near you.

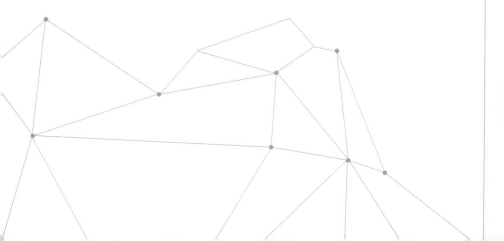

TASKS:

A few resources for this research are found below. Feel free to use additional resources. Record all information you discover in your Cross-Cultural Notebook (Lesson 8).

- Find your country or region on a world map.

- Learn basic facts about your country: topography, climate, major cities, rural areas, flora and fauna, exports and imports, occupations, average income, education, type of government, health care, languages spoken, etc.

- Research religions within your people group or country. What religions do you find represented and at what percentage of the population? Is there an evangelical missionary presence in this group? A missionary presence from another religion?

- If you are looking at a particular people group, do specific research on that group: How is this people group received by others within the society? What percentage of the overall population belongs to this people group?

- Find out if there are any missionaries connected with your church who are working with this group of people and contact them to see if they would be willing to have you interview them. Make a list of questions to ask them to learn more about the culture and the ministry there.

DISCUSS WITH YOUR MENTOR:

- Share your discoveries with your mentor.

- Continue to pray together about where God would have you go.

- Ask your mentor how they learned about the groups they have worked with.

RESOURCES:

Centers for Disease Control: http://www.cdc.gov

Countries of the World: http://www.infoplease.com/countries.html

Joshua Project: http://www.joshuaproject.net

Operation World: http://www.operationworld.org

The World Fact Book - CIA: http://bit.ly/PYCCIAFactBook

YOUR THOUGHTS:

LESSON 21

FREEDOM OF SELF-FORGETFULNESS

FORGETTING ABOUT YOURSELF TO SERVE OTHERS

Have you ever known someone who was proud or arrogant? We aren't usually attracted to people who boast about themselves or their accomplishments. Yet, have you ever known someone with low self-esteem? Neither are we attracted to people who constantly put themselves down.

So, how are we to think of ourselves? Ah, a trick question. The issue is just that—thinking of ourselves. In his book *The Freedom of Self-Forgetfulness*, Timothy Keller speaks to C.S. Lewis' reference to pride from *Mere Christianity* by saying, "Gospel-humility is not thinking more of myself or thinking less of myself, it is thinking of myself less."[3]

TASKS:

Read *The Freedom of Self-Forgetfulness* by Timothy Keller.

Think through the answers to the following questions and prepare to discuss them with your mentor, as well as any other thoughts you have:

[3] Timothy Keller, *The Freedom of Self-Forgetfulness: The Path to True Christian Joy* (Leyland, England: 10Publishing, 2014), 32.

- In what ways do you struggle to want recognition?

- In what ways do you think poorly of yourself?

- What thoughts come to mind when you consider thinking of yourself less?

- How might thinking of yourself less affect your relationships?

- What are some things you might be able to more fully enjoy, as God's creation, if the focus was less on yourself?

- What difference will this knowledge make in your life?

DISCUSS WITH YOUR MENTOR:

Discuss your responses to the questions above with your mentor.

RESOURCES:

The Freedom of Self-Forgetfulness: The Path to True Christian Joy
by Timothy Keller
Published by 10Publishing in Leyland, England, 2014.

YOUR THOUGHTS:

_____

_____

_____

_____

LESSON 22
DAY WITH GOD

SPENDING TIME AWAY WITH YOUR CREATOR AND SUSTAINER

Christ's physical ministry on earth lasted only three years. Yet, in this time He often removed Himself to pray.

> *But now even more the report about him went abroad, and great crowds gathered to hear him and to be healed of their infirmities. But he would withdraw to desolate places and pray.*

Luke 5:15-16

As you practice these missional habits and take steps to equip yourself for missions, it is important to set aside time for an overnight spiritual retreat or a day alone with God. This is a time for you to pray and spend time with your heavenly Father.

Go back to Lesson 11, where you learned about "Pathways to God." Consider your pathways and plan how to incorporate one or two of them into your day alone with God. Many people choose to fast during their day with God and remove themselves from their everyday responsibilities. You can go to a park or another place.

Remember that these times are for you to spend with God and not times to work on projects. Before you start, write down all the things that are on your mind and leave them ready for you when you come back. If you can, spend the day without your phone or connection to the internet and all the distractions that come with it.

TASKS:

Look at your schedule and plan a day alone with God. (You might want to consider doing this with your mentor.)

Once you've had your day, talk to your mentor about how it went.

- What did you do that was helpful?

- Was anything about this day difficult for you?

- What did the Lord show you through this time alone with Him?

Plan your next day alone with God, whether it be monthly, quarterly, or biannually. Be sure to block off the day(s) and guard it/them carefully.

DISCUSS WITH YOUR MENTOR:

- What have they experienced in their alone times with God?

- How will you implement this in your life?

- What will your future days with God look like?

- Ask your mentor to hold you accountable to your plans and frequency.

RESOURCES:

R3 Coaching: DAWG Day (Day Alone With God) with Paul Anthes and R3 Coaching, found on *Vimeo*, **http://bit.ly/PYCDAWG**.

"Spending a Day with the Lord" by Ryan Berg, found on *CRU*, **http://bit.ly/PYCDWLord**.

"How to Spend a Day with the Lord" by Katherine Kehler, found on *The Life*, **http://bit.ly/PYCSDWL**.

"How to Spend Extended Time in Prayer" by Navigators, **http://bit.ly/PYCETOP**.

"Spending a Half Day with the Lord" by Tom Virtue, found on *StartingwithGod.com*, **http://bit.ly/PYCKnowGod**.

YOUR THOUGHTS:

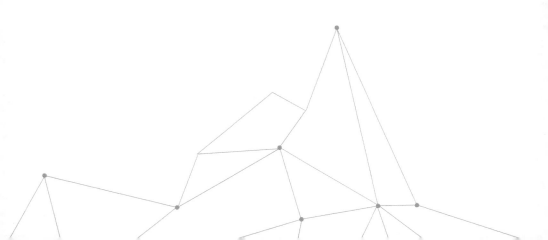

LESSON 23
SPIRITUAL WARFARE AROUND ME

DISCERNING THE SPIRITUAL REALITIES AROUND ME

The principal obstacles that prevent the nations from becoming true worshipers of God are not the barriers of geography, language, and culture. These can be overcome through sacrifice, discipline, and hard work. The principal barriers are spiritual.

After learning about the realities within you, you are more prepared to discern those around you or in other cultures. One of the great lies Satan has given Western civilization is that the spiritual world doesn't exist. By contrast, people in Eastern and African cultures are keenly aware of how much Satan and his forces are at work, fearing what the spiritual forces will do to them next.

Neither fear nor forgetfulness is a healthy response to the dark forces at work. As Christians, we know the One who is in control of everything. He sets us free from fear (Hebrews 2:14) and reminds us to be vigilant against the roaring lion that seeks to devour us (1 Peter 5:8-9).

TASKS:

- Read *Bondage Breaker* by Neil Anderson or *The Three Princes* by Tom Julien.

- Prepare to discuss the spiritual warfare that you have seen around you and how Jesus has given you victory over it.

- Start thinking about the spiritual warfare around you in your daily interactions or with your friends and contacts (distractions, sudden illness, irrational emotions, etc.).

- Considering the people group or culture that you studied in Lesson 20, research that culture's spiritual strongholds (major religion, do they interact with demons or spiritual powers, what lies do they believe, etc.).

- Consider an exploratory trip to the place and people God has placed on your heart. Maybe you've already been there, and if so, what spiritual strongholds did you observe firsthand? If you haven't been there, talk to your mobilizer about opportunities to pursue this as a next step.

- Begin praying for victory in the spiritual warfare that you see. Remember to pray for the Christians there as well as for your own preparation.

DISCUSS WITH YOUR MENTOR:

- Talk with your mentor about the spiritual warfare you have seen in your life and the victories that Jesus has given you. (Lesson 12)

- What spiritual warfare do you see in your culture and how does this affect you and your current ministry?

- The enemy does not play fair. How have you seen Satan at work in destroying Christians' ministry and witness?

- How can you prepare for encountering the strongholds that exist in other cultures?

RESOURCES:

The Bondage Breaker by Neil Anderson
Published by Harvest House Publishers in Eugene, OR, 2019.

The Three Princes: Lifting the Veil on the Unseen World by Tom Julien
Published by BMH Books in Winona Lake, IN, 2011.

YOUR THOUGHTS:

LESSON 24
REFLECT AND PROCESS

Congratulations, you've made it to the last lesson. This final chapter is the chance to look back and think about the missional habits you're learning and practicing. Remember, implementing these and inviting others to do the same is helpful no matter where you are in the world.

- Have you had an opportunity to share about Jesus and what He has done in your life with anyone recently? If not, how can you seek opportunities to do this?

- Are you building on the habits and skills you developed in Parts 1 and 2?

- What steps have you taken in Part 3 that have benefitted you?

- What skill or habit has been particularly difficult for you to incorporate?

- Discuss these reflections with your mentor, specifically the habits you want to grow in and the steps you're taking to do so.

- Meet with a mobilizer to talk about what you learned and how it could apply to a future ministry opportunity. Email **GO@EncompassWorld.org** to talk with a mobilizer.

YOUR THOUGHTS:

CONCLUSION
NEXT STEPS

Pursuing Your Calling is not the end, but merely the beginning of what we hope will be a lifetime of intentional, missional living. The missional habits that you have practiced are meant to help you mature in Christ and be a witness for Him wherever you are, but especially in a cross-cultural context.

Continue to implement these habits as you seek to be a curious learner. We hope you will continue this journey throughout life, and that as you pursue your calling, it will be with a deeper understanding of what God has for you in the application of these principles. Continue in the journey by meeting regularly with your local mentor, pastor, and mobilizer to confirm the next steps God has for you. Our prayer is that God will use these lessons and practices to form you even more into the likeness of Jesus as you continue to *pursue your calling*.

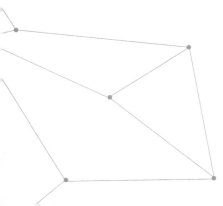

APPENDIX 1

BIBLICAL FOUNDATIONS

What biblical knowledge and training do cross-cultural workers need? The answers are as varied as the roles and responsibilities of the workers who serve on the mission field. However, there is a base of knowledge for anyone serving in cross-cultural ministry. We want to provide an outline and offer resources as you seek to prepare for ministry.

Keep in mind there are three major factors that should be considered when developing a plan for growth in the Biblical Foundations:

- What training you have already completed in these areas

- What resources your church offers to train people for ministry

- What kind of cross-cultural ministry you're moving toward

It's our goal to work with you on a customized plan for how to move through this concurrently with the other lessons in *Pursuing Your Calling*.

TOPICS FOR BIBLICAL FOUNDATIONS:

- **Introduction to the Bible:** The ability to defend the historicity, source, and story of the Bible.

- **Bible Study Methods and Interpretation:** How to understand and apply biblical truth.

- **Old Testament Survey:** Overview of the OT including cultural, historical, and main ideas of each book.

- **New Testament Survey:** Overview of the NT including cultural, historical, and main ideas of each book.

- **Introduction to Systematic Theology:** An overview of theology.

  - Theology Proper - Study of God

  - Christology - Study of Christ

  - Pneumatology - Study of the Holy Spirit

  - Soteriology - Study of Salvation

  - Ecclesiology - Study of the Church

  - Eschatology – Study of the End Times

RECOMMENDATIONS AND RESOURCES FOR BIBLICAL FOUNDATIONS:

Recommendations for a Customized Plan for Formal or Informal Options

Along with the input of your church, a recommendation from your mobilizer or training mentor can determine the best option for you based on your current circumstances and the ministry opportunity you are moving toward. We will help you customize a plan to grow in the Biblical Foundations and be ready to move into ministry.

Below is a list of recommended options, but there are many other great opportunities worth pursuing. For those seeking informal or independent study options, we can help you create a plan based on what might be available through your church and a combination of the resources recommended below.

Formal Degree Programs Both Residential and Online

- ### *Grace College & Seminary*

  Grace College is an evangelical Christian community of higher education which applies biblical values in strengthening character, sharpening competence, and preparing for service. Grace Theological Seminary is a learning community dedicated to teaching, training, and transforming the whole person for local church and global ministry. They have an Intercultural Studies and Global Languages major. Undergraduate and graduate programs are available on campus or online, and the seminary offers a unique mentored program called *Deploy*.
  Learn more at **www.grace.edu**.

- ### *Eternity Bible College*

  Eternity exists to glorify God through graduates whose lives are transformed by rigorous study of the Bible as Scripture, impassioned love for God, and gracious service in the church for the world. Eternity is committed to helping students graduate without incurring college debt so they can pursue God's calling on their lives without that burden. Students can choose to pursue a Bachelor of Biblical Studies, as well as one- or two-year certificate and associate degree options. All degree options are available on campus or online. Learn more at **www.eternitybiblecollege.com**.

- ***Moody Bible Institute***

  Moody exists to equip people with the truth of God's Word to be maturing followers of Christ who are making disciples around the world. Moody is a fully accredited Bible school with campuses in Chicago, Illinois and Spokane, Washington; seminary campuses in Chicago, Illinois and Plymouth, Michigan; and online Bible degrees and distance learning options. For residential undergraduate students preparing to serve in vocational ministry, tuition is free. Learn more at **www.moody.edu**.

- ***Great Commission Bible Institute***

  GCBI is a ten-month discipleship program geared toward young adults and is designed to create a solid understanding of God's Word and a broad experience in discipleship and ministry. Through biblical studies courses and ministry involvement with the local church, GCBI prepares men and women for the next step, be it pursuing vocational ministry, furthering their education, or entering the workforce or mission field. Learn more at **www.gcbi.net**.

Informal or Independent Study Options Recommended with Mentoring

- ***The Silo Project***

  The Silo Project from Eternity Bible College offers solid teaching from the Bible in affordable, self-paced video courses that are both challenging and easy to understand. You can work through material on your own, with a group from your church, or with other people from around the world. Access all courses through a monthly subscription. Learn more at **www.thesiloproject.org**.

- ***One Hour One Book.***

  One Hour One Book from Great Commission Bible Institute offers the teachings of Dr. Randall D. Smith covering all 66 books of the Bible each in a one-hour video format. It represents a condensed version of what GCBI offers through its residential program and can be done at your own pace from anywhere in the world. Learn more at **www.1hour1book.com**.

- ***Bible Doctrines: Essential Teachings of the Christian Faith***
  by Wayne Grudem

  Bible Doctrines takes a highly recommended upper-level textbook on systematic theology and makes it accessible to the average reader. Abridged from Wayne Grudem's award-winning Systematic Theology, Bible Doctrines covers the same essentials of the faith, giving the reader a firm grasp of seven key topics: The Doctrine of the Word of God, The Doctrine of God, The Doctrine of Man, The Doctrine of Christ, The Doctrine of the Application of Redemption, The Doctrine of the Church, and The Doctrine of the Future. We recommend going through this with your mentor. You can order the book online.

- ***Introducing Christian Doctrines*** by Millard J. Erickson (Second Edition)

  Introducing Christian Doctrines is an abridged, less technical version of Millard J. Erickson's classic *Christian Theology*. Erickson begins by explaining what theology is and then progresses through the doctrines of revelation, God, creation and providence, humanity, sin, Jesus Christ, the Holy Spirit, the atonement and salvation, the church, and eschatology. We recommend going through this with your mentor. You can order the book online.

- ***Truth Quest:* The Search for Spiritual Understanding**, *a community-based doctrinal discovery system developed by Neil Cole*

  Truth Quest is a discovery system designed to equip leaders to continue the journey of learning for the rest of their lives. It not only teaches, but it can also easily reproduce and multiply into the lives of succeeding generations. It requires a class size between four and eight and one facilitator. Students meet one day per month for a year to be prepared to think theologically, but also to pass that education on to others. If you enjoy group learning and your church can support a group, it is an enriching process. Learn more at **https://bit.ly/PYCTruthquest**.

- ***Ministry Ordination or Credentialing Process***

  Most churches or denominations have an ordination process that requires the study of the Bible and articulation of Bible knowledge that's needed to ordain or credential ministers. Some cross-cultural ministry opportunities might require or strongly recommend that one go through this process.

APPENDIX 2

COMPETENCIES & QUALIFICATIONS

The qualifications below represent a list of generally sought-after prerequisites for joining a missions agency. As you complete *Pursuing Your Calling*, many of these competencies will have been covered. It is our hope that the good missional habits that you have put in place will show as you go through this list. Think of where you were before these lessons and be encouraged.

COMPETENCIES:

- **Spiritual Life and Worldview:** Evidences a genuine spiritual life, communicates an understanding of spiritual identity, has accurate perception of spiritual realities, practices disciplines considering these realities and knows how to respond to them

- **Life Balance:** Currently has healthy relationships, is growing self-understanding and awareness, has personal security in Christ, displays growing ability to organize and prioritize relationships, family, finances, work, and ministry in order to sustain personal vitality and influence in the spheres of family and ministry

- **Teamwork:** Displays self-motivation, relational ability, appreciation of diversity and spiritual gifting under recognized leadership, organization of work and time, sound financial management, evidence of conflict resolution and restoration of relationships

- **Contact-Making/Evangelism:** Demonstrates an evangelistic lifestyle using culturally-appropriate forms of contact-making and evangelism

- **Discipleship/Spiritual Reproduction:** Demonstrates spiritual disciplines and reproduction in others (who will reproduce in others)

- **Understanding of and Living the Essence of Church:** Shows commitment to the church, has growing ability to differentiate between the essence and expression of the church, with participation in a local spiritual family, developing skills critical to creating and fostering new spiritual families

- **Handling Scripture:** Shows growth in knowledge, application, and teaching of the Bible in culturally-appropriate ways

QUALIFICATIONS:

- Spiritual and personal growth

- College degree or equivalent experience (not all ministries require a degree; some require advanced degrees; some visas require a degree)

- Cross-culture ministry experience beyond just vacations, either domestically or internationally

- Some formal biblical training (refer to Appendix 1: Biblical Foundations)

- Relevant ministry experience both inside and outside the church

- Home church support and pastoral recommendation

- Consumer debt freedom (most agencies allow for qualified educational debt; talk to your mobilizer for more information)

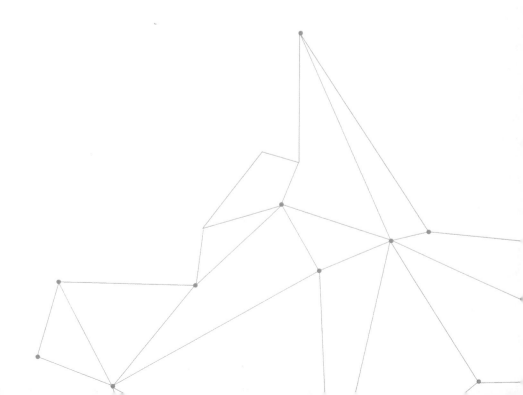

WHAT CAN I DO NOW TO PREPARE FOR FUTURE CROSS-CULTURAL MINISTRY?

Now is a time to learn and develop the foundational tools required for future ministry. *Pursuing Your Calling* is a mentored discipleship guide designed for use in a local church context with the goal of forming the missional habits that are needed for cross-cultural ministry. The book includes 24 lessons that focus on applying eight missional habits.

IN THIS BOOK, YOU'LL LEARN:

- The missional habits essential to thriving in cross-cultural ministry

- How to develop your strengths and gifts

- How to manage life and ministry while avoiding burnout

- Ways to cultivate your partners and supporters

ABOUT THE SERIES:

Pursuing Your Calling is part of a series titled *The Path: Navigating the Journey to Global Missions.* This series presents three tools or applications, with this book serving as the "compass" that orients you as you continue your journey. At the conclusion of this book, you will have learned and applied many of the essential missional habits of successful global workers. You will be challenged to take the next step along the path toward going.

NAVIGATE THE JOURNEY TO GLOBAL MISSIONS

Just as travel tools and resources guide you to destinations, give you insights, and point the way, the books in *The Path Series* will help you explore your calling and navigate the journey to global missions.

Encompass™ WORLD PUBLISHING

Learn more and purchase online // PATHSERIES.COM

Made in the USA
Columbia, SC
26 August 2020

16346474R00073